Weight Watchers™

GOOD FOOD *FAST!*

Cas Clarke

SIMON & SCHUSTER

A VIACOM COMPANY

First published in Great Britain by Simon & Schuster, 1999
A Viacom Company

Simon & Schuster UK Ltd
Africa House
64-78 Kingsway
London WC2B 6SX

Design: Moore Lowenhoff
Cover design: Jane Humphrey
Typesetting: Stylize Digital Artwork
Photography: Steve Baxter
Styling: Marian Price
Food preparation: Jane Stevenson

Weight Watchers Publications Manager: Elizabeth Egan
Weight Watchers Publications Assistant: Celia Whiston

A CIP catalogue record is available from the British Library

ISBN: 0 684 85860 6

Printed in Hong Kong

Pictured on the front cover: *Lemon Chicken Risotto (page 29)*

Pictured on the back cover: *Chocolate Mousse with Nut 'n' Cherry Topping (page 77)*

Recipe notes:
Egg size is medium, unless otherwise stated.
Fruit and vegetables are medium-sized, unless otherwise stated.
It is important to use proper measuring spoons, not cutlery, for spoon measures.
1 tablespoon = 15 ml; 1 teaspoon = 5 ml.
Dried herbs can be substituted for fresh ones, but the flavour may not always
be as good. Halve the fresh herb quantity stated in the recipe.

v shows the recipe is suitable for vegetarians.

Contents

Introduction

Thousands of people have discovered that the Weight Watchers Programme really works for them and now with 123 Success 2000™ it is even easier to lose weight. It works so well because Weight Watchers recipes are designed to show that dieting isn't just about losing weight – it's about switching to a new way of eating which encourages you to eat more of the things that are good for you such as fresh fruit and vegetables, and to cut down on fatty foods.

We are lucky to live in modern times when so many low-fat alternatives are available to us – it has never been easier to reduce our fat intake and still enjoy our meals. By switching to a healthier way of eating, it is much easier to keep weight off and in later life we will reap the benefits of changing to a healthier diet.

We are encouraged to eat more fresh fruit and vegetables, but because they require some preparation and should be bought as fresh as possible, they are not always easy to fit into our busy lifestyles. Canned or frozen fruit and vegetables are a good alternative though and sometimes the nutritional value is actually higher than it is in 'fresh' produce. Peas are a good example – it is unlikely that the fresh peas in the shops are as nutritious as the frozen variety. So even if we don't eat fresh produce every day, we can still have a healthier diet by including more canned or frozen vegetables in our meals.

As a mother of two small children I know how difficult it can be to find the time to produce healthy yet tasty meals for all the family. But this book is full of recipes which are not only quick and easy to make, but also delicious and sure to please. One new product that I have found to be invaluable for cutting down on fat is cooking oil that you just spray on to pans. A whole range of low-fat cooking sprays are widely available and worth their weight in gold since they make it easy to fry foods with a minimum of fat. Make sure that this is on your next shopping list!

Soups

One of the best ways to include plenty of fresh vegetables in your diet is to enjoy more homemade soup. Soups are wonderfully versatile and they are quick and easy to make. You can include a variety of vegetables and then mix and match with other ingredients to make a filling and hearty lunch or light meal. They are wonderful with a side salad and some crusty bread or rolls and are an ideal way to enjoy healthy and nutritious food.

Mushroom Soup

Serves: 4

Preparation time: 10 minutes + 10 minutes cooking
Calories per serving: with crème fraîche 60; without crème fraîche 50

Freezing: not recommended

It is really quick and easy just to tip the mushrooms into a food processor and quickly whiz them round to chop them. Otherwise, it will take about 5 minutes to finely chop all the mushrooms!

250 g (9 oz) closed cup mushrooms, chopped finely
1 garlic clove, crushed
500 ml (18 fl oz) vegetable stock, made with 1 stock cube and boiling water
150 ml (5 fl oz) skimmed milk
2 tablespoons cornflour
1 tablespoon half-fat crème fraîche (optional)

1. Put the finely chopped mushrooms, garlic and stock in a medium saucepan and bring to the boil. Cover and simmer for 10 minutes.
2. Liquidise and add 100 ml (3¹/₂ fl oz) milk. Return to the heat.
3. Blend the cornflour with the remaining 50 ml (2 fl oz) milk and add to the pan. Stir until the soup thickens.
4. Take off the heat, stir through the crème fraîche, if using, and serve.

Points per serving: with crème fraîche 1; without crème fraîche ¹/₂
Total Points per recipe: with crème fraîche 3; without crème fraîche 2¹/₂

Hearty Vegetable Soup

Serves: 2

Preparation time: 10 minutes
+ 20 minutes cooking
Calories per serving: 270

Freezing: not recommended

Ⓥ if using vegetable stock

Although I prefer to make this main course soup with chicken stock, you could make a vegetarian version with vegetable stock.

1 onion, chopped
400 g (14 oz) potatoes, diced
2 large carrots, chopped
2 celery sticks, sliced
850 ml (1½ pints) chicken or vegetable stock, made from 1 stock cube and boiling water
200 g (7 oz) canned butter beans, well rinsed and drained
freshly ground black pepper

1. Put the onion, potatoes, carrots, celery and stock into a medium saucepan. Bring to the boil, cover and then simmer for 20 minutes until the vegetables are cooked.
2. Place half the soup with half of the butter beans in a liquidiser and blend until smooth.
3. Return to the pan with the rest of the beans. Heat through, season with pepper and serve.

Points per serving: 3½
Total Points per recipe: 7

Creamy Tomato Soup

Serves: 4

Preparation and cooking time: 10 minutes
Calories per serving: 60

Freezing: not recommended

Ⓥ

My two children prefer tomato soup with some tomato ketchup added! Try it and see what your friends or family think.

690 g jar of sieved (passata)
200 g (7 oz) very low-fat plain fromage frais
a pinch of sugar
2 tablespoons tomato ketchup
freshly ground black pepper

1. Put the passata into a medium saucepan and add 300 ml (10 fl oz) cold water. Warm gently but do not boil.
2. When the passata is warm, stir in the fromage frais, sugar and tomato ketchup. Season to taste.
3. Heat through again gently, until the soup returns to serving temperature.

Points per serving: ½
Total Points per recipe: 1½

Cook's notes:
For a more sophisticated flavour, add some fresh herbs, such as basil, chervil or tarragon in step 2.
   This soup could also be chilled and served cold.

Variation:
You can also make this using canned tomatoes – but I find it has a better texture when sieved tomatoes (passata) are used.

Onion Soup with Toasted Cheesy Topping

Serves: 2

Preparation and cooking time: 10 minutes

Calories per serving: 215

Freezing: not recommended

V if using vegetarian cheese

2 × 425 g cans of French onion soup
2 × 5 cm (2-inch) slices of French stick
40 g (1½ oz) half-fat Cheddar cheese, grated
1 teaspoon French mustard
a dash of Worcestershire sauce

A filling soup which is ideal for cold and rainy days.

1. Preheat the grill.
2. Pour the soup into a medium saucepan.
3. Gently heat the soup.
4. Meanwhile toast the bread slices on one side and mash together the grated cheese and French mustard.
5. Turn the toasted breads over and pile the cheese and mustard paste on top. Flatten with a fork and season with a dash of Worcestershire sauce.
6. Grill until the cheese is brown and bubbling.
7. Divide the soup between two serving bowls and top each with a toasted cheese slice.

Points per serving: 4
Total Points per recipe: 8½

Quick Chicken Soup

Serves: 4

Preparation and cooking time: 15 minutes

Calories per serving: 80

Freezing: recommended before the quark is added

This quick soup is perfect for cold winter days.

700 ml (1¼ pints) chicken stock made with 1 stock cube and boiling water
2 medium boneless, skinless chicken breasts, diced
100 ml (3½ fl oz) quark (a virtually-fat-free soft cheese)
2 teaspoons lemon juice
freshly ground black pepper

1. Put the stock and diced chicken in a medium saucepan.
2. Bring to the boil and simmer for 5 minutes.
3. Put the soup in a liquidiser with the quark and blend until smooth.
4. Return to the pan, add the lemon juice and season. Gently heat through but do not boil. Serve.

Points per serving: 1½
Total Points per recipe: 6

Pea and Ham Soup

Serves: 4

Preparation and cooking time:
15 minutes
Calories per serving: 55

**Freezing: recommended before
the fromage frais is added**

ⓥ **if using vegetarian stock
and omitting the ham**

275 g (9¹/₂ oz) frozen peas
1 litre (1³/₄ pints) ham stock
    made from 1 stock cube and
    boiling water
3 tablespoons very low-fat plain
    fromage frais
2 tablespoons cornflour
2 slices of honey roast ham
    (about 70 g/2¹/₂ oz), diced

**For a vegetarian version of
this soup make with vegetable
stock, omit the ham and add
a little mint when cooking
the peas. Points per serving
will be 1¹/₂.**

1. Place the peas and ham stock in a medium saucepan and bring
to the boil. Cover and simmer for 3–4 minutes until the peas are
cooked.
2. Put in a liquidiser with the fromage frais and blend.
3. Mix a little of the soup with the cornflour to make a smooth paste.
4. Pour the soup and the cornflour paste back into the saucepan
over a medium heat and stir until the soup has thickened.
5. Add the diced ham and serve.

Points per serving: 2
Total Points per recipe: 7¹/₂

Vegetable and Turkey Soup

Serves: 4

**Preparation time: 5 minutes +
10 minutes cooling
Calories per serving:** 145

Freezing: not recommended

**Adding this crispy topping
makes for a much more
interesting soup.**

4 × medium turkey rashers
2 × 425 g cans of extra-thick
    vegetable soup

1. Under a hot grill, grill the turkey rashers for 2 minutes on each
side. Cut into thin strips and leave to cool.
2. Meanwhile, spoon the soup into a medium saucepan and heat
gently for 3–4 minutes. Do not allow to boil.
3. Pour the soup into serving bowls and sprinkle the turkey strips
on top to serve.

Points per serving: 2
Total Points per recipe: 8

Snacks and Packed Lunches

If you have to eat at least one meal a day away from home and you're trying to lose weight, it's a good idea to make a deliciously fresh and low-Point lunch at home and take it with you. With the ideas in this chapter you can whip up a packed lunch in no time at all – most of the recipes only take 10 minutes. These lunches and snacks all travel well too, but to avoid any chance of food poisoning (especially in hot weather), it's a good idea to use a cool bag; these are available in many sizes.

Tomato Stuffed with Prawns

Serves: 1

Preparation time: 10 minutes
Calories per serving: 140

Freezing: not recommended

A quick and easy lunch for one but you must plan ahead and remember to defrost the prawns in time!

1 large beefsteak tomato
60 g (2¼ oz) small cocktail prawns, defrosted
4 teaspoons fat-free Thousand Island dressing
lettuce leaves, shredded
freshly ground black pepper

1. Cut a 'lid' off the tomato and scoop out the inside. Discard the seeds and chop up the flesh.
2. Mix the chopped tomato flesh with the prawns and dressing. Season and use to stuff the tomato.
3. Replace the 'lid' and serve on a bed of shredded lettuce leaves.

Points per serving: 1
Total Points per recipe: 1

Cook's note:
If you can find it, try to use the Kraft dressing – it has the best flavour and texture.

Avocado and Tomato Salsa Sandwich

Serves: 2

Preparation time: 5 minutes
Calories per serving: 180

Freezing: not recommended

Simply halve the ingredients to make this a dish for one.

2 medium slices of wholemeal bread
1 tablespoon 90% fat-free Weight Watchers from Heinz mayonnaise-style dressing
lettuce leaves, shredded
1 baby avocado or half an avocado (about 85 g/3 oz), peeled and sliced thinly
2 tablespoons Heinz ready-made tomato salsa

1. Place the bread on two serving plates.
2. Spread the mayonnaise dressing (this helps to 'anchor' the lettuce) on to the bread.
3. Cover with the lettuce and then with slices of avocado.
4. Spoon a tablespoon of tomato salsa over each portion and serve.

Points per serving: 2½
Total Points per recipe: 5

Cook's notes:
If you have some leftover avocado, leave the stone in to prevent it from going black. Put it in an airtight container but do not put it in the refrigerator. It will keep for a day or two.

Avocado and Cottage Cheese Dip

Serves: 1

Preparation time: 5 minutes
Calories per serving: 180

Freezing: not recommended

This is a good way to use up leftover avocado.

½ baby avocado (about 40 g/ 1½ oz), peeled and mashed
115 g (4 oz) plain diet cottage cheese
freshly ground black pepper

1. Combine the avocado and cottage cheese and season.

Points per serving: 3
Total Points per recipe: 3

Variation:
This makes a great dip for crudités or a delicious topping for an open sandwich.

Cheesy Dip with Veggie Sticks

Serves: 2

Preparation time: 10 minutes
Calories per serving: 100

Freezing: not recommended

 if using vegetarian cheese

This is a lovely, fresh-tasting dip.

115 g (4 oz) plain diet cottage cheese
50 g (1¾ oz) low-fat soft cheese
2 celery sticks, trimmed and cut into matchsticks
5 cm (2-inch) piece of cucumber, cut into matchsticks
½ green pepper, de-seeded and cut into matchsticks
a few cauliflower florets
a few button mushrooms
freshly grated black pepper

1. Combine the cheeses, season with pepper and put in a small serving bowl.
2. Serve the dip with the vegetables.

Points per serving: 1½
Total Points per recipe: 3

Cook's note:
I often add a clove of crushed garlic for extra flavour.

...d Onion Open Sandwich

Preparation time: 5 minutes
Calories per serving: 105

Freezing: not recommended

(V) if using vegetarian cheese

This is delicious with slices of tomato.

1 medium slice of wholemeal
  bread
1 teaspoon 90% fat-free Weight
  Watchers from Heinz
  mayonnaise-style dressing
lettuce leaves, shredded
115 g (4 oz) plain diet cottage
  cheese
2.5 cm (1-inch) piece of
  cucumber, skinned and diced
2–3 spring onions, chopped
  finely
freshly ground black pepper

1. Place the bread on a serving plate and spread with the mayonnaise dressing. Top with the shredded lettuce leaves.
2. Mix together the cottage cheese, cucumber and spring onions in a small bowl.
3. Pile this mixture on to the lettuce and season.

Points per serving: 2¹/₂

Cook's note:
I think this is improved with a sprinkling of ground cayenne which adds an attractive finishing touch to the dish.

Chilli Tortillas

Serves: 4

Preparation and cooking time:
10 minutes
Calories per serving: 215

Freezing: not recommended

(V) if using vegetarian cheese

These tortillas make a great lunch with some salad on the side.

215 g can of chilli beans
4 medium-sized flour tortillas
  or pitta breads
40 g (1¹/₂ oz) reduced-fat
  Cheddar cheese, grated
4 teaspoons half-fat crème
  fraîche

1. Gently heat the beans in a small saucepan. Wrap the tortillas or pittas in foil and warm in a preheated oven. Or to speed things up, wrap them in microfilm and warm for 40 seconds in the microwave.
2. When both the beans and the tortillas have been warmed through, lay the tortillas out on the serving plates and divide the beans and cheese among them evenly. Top each tortilla with a teaspoon of crème fraîche and roll up. If using pitta bread, divide up the beans and cheese evenly and fill the pitta pockets with them. Add a teaspoon of crème fraîche. Serve immediately.

Points per serving: with tortilla 3¹/₂; with pitta 4
Total Points per recipe: with tortilla 13¹/₂; with pitta 15¹/₂

Banana Salad

Serves: 1

Preparation time: 5 minutes
Calories per serving: with sunflower seeds 285; with almonds 235

Freezing: not recommended

A very tasty and healthy lunch dish which travels well if you add the banana and mayonnaise dressing just before serving.

mixed lettuce leaves, shredded
1 or 2 celery sticks, trimmed and sliced thinly
2.5 cm (1-inch) piece of cucumber, halved and sliced
1 medium banana, sliced
1 tablespoon raisins
1 tablespoon sunflower seeds or 1 tablespoon toasted flaked almonds
4 teaspoons 90% fat-free Weight Watchers from Heinz mayonnaise-style dressing

1. Put the mixed salad leaves into a serving bowl and add the celery and cucumber.
2. Top with the banana and raisins. Add the sunflower seeds or toasted almonds.
3. Dress your salad with the mayonnaise dressing and enjoy!

Points per serving: with sunflower seeds 4; with almonds 4$\frac{1}{2}$

Tomato and Cheese Salad

Serves: 2

Preparation time: 5 minutes + 20 minutes marinating
Calories per serving: 185

Freezing: not recommended

Ⓥ if using vegetarian cheese

This can be part of a wonderful low-Point lunch for two on a hot summer's day. Enjoy it with a couple of French stick slices to help mop up the salad dressing and then finish off with some fresh summer fruits, adding the extra Points.

2 extra-large tomatoes (beefsteak tomatoes), sliced
8 cherry tomatoes, halved
85 g (3 oz) half-fat mozzarella, sliced thinly
20 olives (in brine), rinsed, drained, stoned and cut into strips or 50 g (1$\frac{3}{4}$ oz) sliced olives in brine, well rinsed and drained
4 tablespoons Weight Watchers from Heinz Tomato and Basil dressing

1. Arrange the tomato and cheese slices on two serving plates.
2. Sprinkle over the olives and drizzle the tomato and basil dressing on top.
3. Leave for 20 minutes to let the flavours develop and then serve.

Points per serving: 2$\frac{1}{2}$
Total Points per recipe: 5$\frac{1}{2}$

Pasta and Tomato Salad

Serves: 1

Preparation and cooking time:
15 minutes
Calories per serving: 45

Freezing: not recommended

**This salad also travels well
so it is ideal for picnics or
packed lunches.**

35 g (1¼ oz) pasta spirals
4 teaspoons Weight Watchers
   from Heinz Tomato and
   Basil dressing
2 tomatoes, sliced or 8 cherry
   tomatoes, halved
10 olives (in brine), rinsed,
   drained, stoned and sliced or
   25 g (1 oz) sliced olives in
   brine, well rinsed and
   drained

1. Cook the pasta according to the packet instructions.
2. Once the pasta is cooked, cool it quickly by putting it in cold water and then drain well.
3. Mix the pasta with all the other ingredients and serve.

Points per serving: 3½

Cook's note:
This keeps well in the refrigerator so why not make double the quantity and use some as a packed lunch the next day?

Variation:
Add 50 g (2 oz) sliced sun-dried tomatoes. If they are not in oil, these will not add any Points.

Mushroom Potatoes

Serves: 2

Preparation time: 5 minutes
+ cooking time for potatoes
Calories per serving: 185

Freezing: not recommended

V if Worcestershire sauce is omitted

2 baking potatoes (about 175 g/
   6 oz each)
300 g (10½ oz) canned and
   sliced cooked mushrooms,
   drained, rinsed and chopped
   finely
50 g (1¾ oz) low-fat soft cheese
a dash of Worcestershire sauce
freshly ground black pepper

1. Cook the baking potatoes for 10–12 minutes in the microwave or for 1–1½ hours in a conventional oven at Gas Mark 6/200°C/400°F.
2. Mix the mushrooms with the soft cheese and season with the Worcestershire sauce and black pepper.
3. Slit open the jacket potatoes and top with the cheese mixture to serve.

Points per serving: 3
Total Points per recipe: 5½

Variation:
To save even more Points, you could use quark instead of the low-fat soft cheese. The Points would be 2½ per serving.

Savoury Banana Sandwich

Serves: 1

Preparation time: 5 minutes
Calories per serving: 280

Freezing: not recommended

I know this sounds unusual
but it really is delicious.
If using for a packed lunch,
put it in an airtight container
to stop the banana turning
brown.

1 medium ripe banana, mashed
1/2–1 teaspoon Marmite
2 medium slices of wholemeal
    bread

1. Mash together the banana and the Marmite.
2. Spoon on to one slice of the bread and flatten with a fork.
3. Top with the other slice of bread.
4. Cut into triangles and serve.

Points per serving: 3½

Variation:
Try adding 1 tablespoon of sunflower seeds to the banana mixture.
This will increase the Points to 4.

Cheese and Celery-Filled Bap

Serves: 1

Preparation time: 5 minutes
Calories per serving: 195

Freezing: recommended

V if using vegetarian cheese

25 g (1 oz) low-fat soft cheese
10 g (1/4 oz) half-fat Cheddar,
    diced
1/2 celery stick, trimmed and
    diced
1 large stoneground wholemeal
    bap, sliced in half
freshly ground black pepper

1. In a small bowl, mix together the cheeses and the celery.
2. Pile the mixture on to one half of the bap and flatten with a fork.
3. Sprinkle with the pepper and top with the other half of the bap.

Points per serving: 5½

Variation:
This filling could also be used to stuff mini pitta breads. Each mini
pitta is worth 1 Point.

Chilli Bean Spread

Serves: 2

Preparation time: 5 minutes
Calories per serving: 90

Freezing: not recommended

This tasty spread for crispbreads, sandwiches or rolls will keep for 24 hours in an airtight container in the refrigerator.

215 g can of beans in chilli sauce
extra chilli seasoning, such as tabasco, chopped fresh chilli or chilli sauce

1. Strain the beans in a sieve which is placed over a bowl so that the sauce is caught in the bowl.
2. Mash the beans thoroughly.
3. Add 1 or 2 teaspoons of the strained chilli sauce to get the beans to a spreading consistency.

Points per serving: 1½
Total Points per recipe: 2½

Cook's note:
Chilli fiends can add some extra chilli seasoning without affecting the Points.

Chicken and Caesar Wrap

Serves: 1

Preparation time: 5 minutes
Calories per serving: 180

Freezing: not recommended

This version has much lower Points per serving than the one you'll find in the supermarket.

lettuce leaf, shredded
1 small wheat tortilla
25 g (1 oz) wafer-thin cooked chicken
1 cherry tomato, sliced
2 teaspoons Weight Watchers from Heinz low-fat Caesar dressing
freshly ground black pepper

1. Place the shredded lettuce on the tortilla, top with the chicken and finish with slices of tomato.
2. Spoon over the dressing, season and then roll up your tortilla, tucking in the bottom so that you make a little pouch which will stop the filling from falling out!

Points per serving: 1½
Total Points per recipe: 1½

Family Meals

One of the most enjoyable things about family life is sitting down together to share a meal. And Weight Watchers recipes are so filling and tasty that everyone can enjoy them. Some of the dishes in this chapter will be very popular with young children who really only like plain food and there are others which will suit more adventurous tastes. There are also a few which are good enough for entertaining such as Lemon Chicken Risotto or Lamb with Creamy Mustard Sauce.

Lemon Chicken Risotto

Serves: 4

Preparation and cooking time:
25 minutes
Calories per serving: 385

Freezing: not recommended

This is an excellent family dish. Serve it with a salad and it can also be a lovely dinner party dish.

700 ml (1¼ pints) chicken stock, made from 1 stock cube and boiling water
250 g (9 oz) risotto rice
low-fat cooking spray
4 medium boneless, skinless chicken breasts, cubed
juice of 1 lemon and 1 tablespoon of the grated rind
40 g (1½ oz) half-fat Cheddar cheese, grated
freshly ground black pepper

1. Place one third of your stock in a saucepan with the risotto rice and bring to the boil. Simmer until virtually all the stock has been absorbed and then add half of the remaining stock.
2. Meanwhile, spray a non-stick frying-pan and fry the chicken. It should take only 4 or 5 minutes to cook and brown the chicken cubes.
3. When the stock has been absorbed, add the lemon juice and grated rind. Add the rest of the stock and the cooked chicken. Cook until almost all the stock has gone. The rice should now be cooked.
4. Stir through the grated cheese, season and serve.

Points per serving: 6½
Total Points per recipe: 25½

and Vegetable Korma

...ne: 10 minutes
+ 20 minutes cooking
Calories per serving: 245

Freezing: recommended

**This mild chicken curry is
wonderful for children.**

low-fat cooking spray
1 onion, sliced thinly
400 g jar of half-fat korma
    curry sauce
4 medium boneless, skinless
    chicken breasts, diced
1 small cauliflower, divided
    into small florets
100 g (3½ oz) frozen peas or
    petit pois

1. Spray a non-stick frying-pan with the low-fat cooking spray and
fry the onion lightly.
2. Add the curry sauce, 200 ml (7 fl oz) cold water, diced chicken
and cauliflower.
3. Bring to the boil, cover tightly and cook on a low heat for 20
minutes.
4. Add the petit pois or peas 5 minutes before the end of the
cooking time.
5. When it has finished cooking, stir well and serve.

Points per serving: 3
Total Points per recipe: 12½

Teriyaki Chicken Stir-Fry

Serves: 4

Preparation and cooking time:
10 minutes + 20 minutes
marinating
Calories per serving: 210

Freezing: not recommended

**When it is cooled this makes
a superb chicken salad. Be
careful not to overcook your
vegetables because they are
best in this recipe when crisp.**

4 medium boneless, skinless
    chicken breasts, cut into
    thin strips
3 tablespoons teriyaki
    marinade
low-fat cooking spray
2 large carrots, cut into small
    matchsticks
1 red pepper, de-seeded and cut
    into small matchsticks
150 g jar of teriyaki stir-fry
    sauce
1 bunch of spring onions,
    chopped

1. Marinate the chicken in the teriyaki marinade for 20 minutes.
2. Spray a non-stick frying-pan with low-fat spray and then tip in
the chicken and marinade. Fry for 2 minutes.
3. Add the carrots and pepper and stir-fry for 4 minutes.
4. Add the sauce and spring onions and warm through.

Points per serving: 3
Total Points per recipe: 12

Triple Tomato Sauce with Pasta

Serves: 3

Preparation and cooking time: 15 minutes	350 g (12 oz) farfalle or pasta of your choice
Calories per serving: 485	400 g (14 oz) canned chopped tomatoes
	1 tablespoon tomato purée
Freezing: recommended for the sauce only	a pinch of sugar
	4 tomatoes, skinned, white core removed and chopped
	freshly ground black pepper

1. Cook the pasta according to the packet instructions. Meanwhile, prepare the tomato sauce.
2. Place the canned tomatoes, tomato purée and sugar in a pan and bring to a gentle simmer.
3. Skin the fresh tomatoes by covering them with boiling water for 30 seconds and then draining them. The skin will peel off easily.
4. When the pasta is cooked, drain and divide between 3 serving bowls.
5. Divide the chopped fresh tomatoes between the serving bowls. Season the cooked tomato sauce and spoon over the serving bowls.

Points per serving: 4
Total Points per recipe: 12

Cook's note:
This can be jazzed up by adding fresh or dried herbs such as basil, marjoram or oregano, which all have a natural affinity with tomatoes.

Variation:
You could also add 2 sliced sun-dried tomatoes which will add no Points if they are not in oil.

Broccoli and Tuna Pasta

Serves: 3

Preparation and cooking time: 15 minutes	175 g (6 oz) broccoli florets
Calories per serving: 280	175 g (6 oz) pasta bows
	185 g can of tuna in brine, rinsed and drained
Freezing: not recommended	salt and freshly ground black pepper

This will serve two adults and two small children. Small children like it because it is plain and simple.

1. Cook the broccoli for 8–10 minutes until tender. Drain.
2. Meanwhile cook the pasta according to the packet instructions.
3. Put the cooked pasta into serving bowls.
4. Divide the tuna among the bowls. Gently fork through the broccoli florets to break them up slightly (but don't mash them) before mixing into the tuna and pasta. Season and serve.

Points per serving: 3
Total Points per recipe: 8½

Curried Beans and Mushrooms

Serves: 3

Preparation and cooking time: 5 minutes

Calories per serving: 105

Freezing: not recommended

Ⓥ

A tasty topping for either jacket potatoes or toast.

400 g (14 oz) canned Weight Watchers from Heinz baked beans
300 g (10½ oz) canned sliced mushrooms, chopped roughly
1 or 2 teaspoons medium balti curry paste, to taste
¼ or ½ teaspoon ground cumin, to taste

1. Put the ingredients in a small saucepan and heat through.
2. Cover and simmer for a few minutes, stirring occasionally.

Points per serving: 1½
Total Points per recipe: 4½

Variation:
Add 2 teaspoons of mango chutney to each portion. This will add 1 Point per serving.

Chicken and Vegetable Pie

Serves: 4

Preparation time: 10 minutes
+ 25 minutes cooking
Calories per serving: 160

Freezing: recommended

I've adapted this lovely pie from a North African dish – now it is quicker and easier to make but equally as delicious.

2 tablespoons cornflour
300 ml (10 fl oz) skimmed milk
low-fat cooking spray
2 medium boneless, skinless chicken breasts, cubed
230 g jar of petits pois and baby carrots, drained and rinsed
2 filo pastry sheets (25 cm/ 10 inches square)
freshly ground black pepper

1. Preheat the oven to Gas Mark 6/200°C/400°F.
2. Make a white sauce by blending the cornflour with 2 tablespoons of the milk. Heat the rest of the milk and then stir in the cornflour paste. Stir as the sauce thickens and cooks.
3. Spray a non-stick frying-pan with cooking spray and stir-fry the chicken until cooked and beginning to brown.
4. Mix together the chicken, sauce and vegetables. Transfer to a pie dish.
5. Season and cover with the 2 sheets of filo, giving each sheet a quick squirt with the low-fat cooking spray. Crumple up the sheet edges around the pie dish. Cut two slits in the top and cook in the oven for 20–25 minutes until a light golden brown colour.

Points per serving: 3
Total Points per recipe: 11½

Fish in a Flash

Serves: 4

Preparation and cooking time:
10 minutes
Calories per serving: 125

Freezing: not recommended

55 g (2 oz) tikka-flavoured
   ready-made marinade
4 × 100 g (3½ oz) frozen
   chunky cod fillets

**Serve with a salad and new
potatoes.**

1. Shake half of the marinade over the fish.
2. Put on a microwave plate. Cover and cook in the microwave for
4 minutes.
3. Turn over and sprinkle with the rest of the marinade. Cover and
cook for a further 4 minutes.

Points per serving: 2
Total Points per recipe: 8½

Cook's note:
Look for the Knorr Marinades-in-Minutes range – they are excellent.

Lamb with Creamy Mustard Sauce

Serves: 4

Preparation and cooking time:
20 minutes
Calories per serving: 120

Freezing: not recommended

4 medium lamb cutlets
4 tablespoons half-fat crème
   fraîche
2 tablespoons skimmed milk
2 teaspoons whole-grain
   mustard
1 teaspoon Dijon mustard

**This sauce is incredibly quick
and easy to make.**

1. Preheat the grill to medium hot.
2. Grill the lamb cutlets for 15–18 minutes, turning after 8 minutes.
3. To make the sauce, gently heat the half-fat crème fraîche with
the milk and stir into a smooth sauce with a wooden spoon.
4. Stir the mustards into the sauce and serve spooned over the
lamb cutlets.

Points per serving: 3
Total Points per recipe: 12

Variation:
Try this delicious sauce with fish or chicken.

Cajun Chicken Strips

Serves: 4

Preparation time: 5 minutes
+ 5 minutes marinating
+ 20 minutes cooking
Calories per serving: 200

Freezing: not recommended

**These can also be cooked on
a barbecue and are excellent
with a salad.**

4 medium boneless, skinless
  chicken breasts, cut into thin
  strips
Cajun-flavoured ready-made
  marinade

1. Preheat the oven to Gas Mark 7/220°C/425°F.
2. Sprinkle the chicken strips with the Cajun marinade and leave
to marinate for 5 minutes.
3. Place the chicken on a baking tray and cook for 20 minutes until
cooked and blackening at the edges.

Points per serving: 3
Total Points per recipe: 12

Cook's note:
Look for the Knorr Marinades-in-Minutes collection.

Variation:
These are also nice cold in picnics or packed lunches.

Beef and Vegetable Pie

Serves: 4

Preparation time: 10 minutes
+ 20 minutes cooking
Calories per serving: 240

Freezing: not recommended

**Kids love this – once they've
added some tomato sauce!**

low-fat cooking spray
350 g (12 oz) extra-lean steak
  mince
25 g (1 oz) gravy granules
300 ml (10 fl oz) boiling water
300 g (10½ oz) canned mixed
  vegetables
a dash of Worcestershire sauce
  (optional)
2 filo pastry sheets (25 cm/
  10 inches square)
salt and freshly ground black
  pepper

1. Preheat the oven to Gas Mark 6/200°C/400°F.
2. Spray a non-stick frying-pan with cooking spray and then fry the
mince for 5 minutes to brown. Drain off any fat.
3. Mix together the gravy granules and the boiling water to make a
thick gravy.
4. Add the gravy, drained vegetables and Worcestershire sauce, if
using, to the mince. Season to taste.
5. Place in an ovenproof pie dish and cover with the filo pastry,
crumpling up the edges and tucking them into the sides of the
dish. Spray briefly with low-fat cooking spray.
6. Bake in the oven for 20 minutes.

Points per serving: 4
Total Points per recipe: 16

Chilli Beef and Vegetables

Serves: 4

Preparation time: 10 minutes
+ 20 minutes cooking
Calories per serving: 260

Freezing: not recommended

Be careful about which chilli sauce you buy since some have twice as many Points per serving in them as others. Serve with rice, pasta or baked potatoes and a crisp green salad adding the Points as necessary.

250 g (9 oz) extra-lean minced beef
1 red pepper, de-seeded and chopped finely
1 green pepper, de-seeded and chopped finely
460 g jar of medium-hot chilli sauce
400 g (14 oz) canned red kidney beans, drained and rinsed well.

1. Brown the mince in a non-stick frying-pan.
2. Add the peppers and stir-fry for a few minutes before adding the sauce and beans.
3. Stir well, cover tightly and simmer for 20 minutes. Stir before serving.

Points per serving: 5
Total Points per recipe: 19

Cook's notes:
If you like your chilli really hot, add some more chilli seasoning such as chopped fresh chilli, tabasco or chilli sauce.
   Homepride's chilli sauce is particularly good in this recipe and low in Points.

Family Frittata

Serves: 4

Preparation and cooking time:
25 minutes
Calories per serving: 130

Freezing: not recommended

ⓥ if using free-range eggs

This filling dish is also delicious with cooked vegetables or a crisp side salad. Make sure you use a frying-pan with a handle that will go under the grill.

200 g (7 oz) new potatoes, diced
1 tablespoon groundnut or olive oil
200 g (7 oz) canned sweetcorn, drained
6 eggs, beaten
salt and freshly ground black pepper

1. Stir-fry the potatoes in the oil for about 10 minutes until they are golden and cooked.
2. Add the sweetcorn. Season the eggs and pour over the potato and sweetcorn mixture.
3. Cook for about 8 minutes until you can see that the eggs are setting around the edges of the pan.
4. Meanwhile, preheat the grill to high. When the frittata has cooked for about 8 minutes, put it under the grill and cook until the top is golden on top.
5. Divide into wedges and serve hot or cold.

Points per serving: 4
Total Points per recipe: 16

Margherita Pizza

Serves: 4

Preparation time: 10 minutes
+ 15 minutes cooking
Calories per serving: 115

Freezing: recommended

**Ⓥ if using vegetarian
mozzarella**

400 g (14 oz) canned chopped
  tomatoes
1 tablespoon tomato purée
a pinch of oregano
30 cm (12-inch) thin pizza base
85 g (3 oz) half-fat mozzarella
  cheese, grated
2 tomatoes, sliced thinly
freshly ground black pepper

**Pizza is something everyone
loves. Cold, leftover pizza
also makes a great treat for
the lunchbox.**

1. Preheat the oven to Gas Mark 7/220°C/425°F.
2. Place the chopped tomatoes, tomato purée and oregano in a pan.
Simmer for 5 minutes until you have a thick, pulpy sauce.
3. Spread the tomato sauce over the pizza base to within half an
inch of the sides. Sprinkle with the cheese and top with the slices
of tomato.
4. Season and place directly on an oven shelf. Bake for 15–20
minutes.

Points per serving: 3½
Total Points per recipe: 14

Variation:
Add 2 sliced, sun-dried tomatoes (not in oil) and some chopped
fresh basil. This won't add any Points.

Greek Salad

Serves: 4

Preparation time: 5 minutes
Calories per serving: 205

Freezing: not recommended

Ⓥ if using vegetarian feta

**If you've been to Greece, this
will bring back memories
of relaxing days on sunny
beaches and romantic
evenings in tavernas!**

1 packet of mixed salad leaves,
  shredded
1 green pepper, de-seeded and
  sliced thinly into rings
½ cucumber, sliced thinly
4 tomatoes, cut into wedges
200 g (7 oz) feta cheese, cubed
20 olives (in brine), rinsed,
  stoned and sliced or 50 g
  sliced olives in brine, well
  rinsed and drained
100 ml (3½ fl oz) fat-free
  vinaigrette
2 tablespoons lemon juice
1 teaspoon Dijon mustard

1. Place the shredded salad leaves, green pepper, cucumber and
tomato wedges in a large salad bowl.
2. Mix in the feta cheese and olives.
3. Put the vinaigrette, lemon juice and mustard in a screw-top jar
and shake well.
4. Pour the vinaigrette mixture over the salad and combine before
serving.

Points per serving: 4½
Total Points per recipe: 17½

Variation:
If you like the taste of onion, in step 1 add a small red onion, either
cut into rings or chopped.

Meals for Two

Here are some fabulous fast and tasty treats for two. Whip up an old favourite such as Cod with Parsley Sauce in no time at all or try a scrumptious variation on a classic such as Coronation Potatoes. These quick and delicious recipes are ideal both for busy week-nights and weekends when you want to enjoy your leisure time but also want a delicious meal to look forward to at the end of the day.

Sweet 'n' Spicy Stir-Fry Vegetables

Serves: 2

Preparation and cooking time:
15 minutes
Calories per serving: 125

Freezing: not recommended

low-fat cooking spray
½ red pepper, de-seeded and cubed
½ green pepper, de-seeded and cubed
1 large carrot, cut into small matchsticks
1 courgette, cut into small matchsticks
4 spring onions, sliced
½ teaspoon minced chilli
160 g jar of sweet and sour stir-fry sauce

1. Spray a non-stick frying-pan with the cooking spray.
2. Heat the pan and stir-fry the vegetables for 4 or 5 minutes.
3. Add the minced chilli and the sweet and sour sauce. Stir-fry for a further minute and serve.

Points per serving: 1½
Total Points per recipe: 2½

Cook's note:
Look out for the Sharwoods stir-fry sauces in your supermarket – their flavour is wonderful.

Variation:
Try substituting the sweet and sour sauce with a szechuen spicy tomato sauce. It has chillis in it and therefore no extra chilli needs to be added. Points per serving would then be 3.

Vegetarian Chilli

Serves: 2

Preparation and cooking time:
30 minutes
Calories per serving: 330

Freezing: not recommended

A quick and easy vegetarian
dish for midweek meals. Serve
with rice, pasta or jacket
potatoes and remember to
add the extra Points.

low-fat cooking spray
1 red pepper, de-seeded and
    cubed
1 large carrot, peeled and diced
200 g (7 oz) mushrooms, sliced
    thickly
460 g jar of medium chilli
    sauce
420 g can of red kidney beans,
    rinsed and drained

1. Spray a non-stick frying-pan with cooking spray and stir-fry
the pepper, carrot and mushrooms for 5 minutes.
2. Add the chilli sauce, cover tightly and simmer gently for
15 minutes.
3. Add the beans and cook for a further 5 minutes.

Points per serving: 5½
Total Points per recipe: 11

Sabzi Curry

Serves: 2

Preparation and cooking time:
20 minutes
Calories per serving: 245

Freezing: recommended

This quick and tasty dish is
sure to become a favourite – it
is just the thing for a midweek
meal.

low-fat cooking spray
100 g (3½ oz) French beans,
    trimmed and halved
100 g (3½ oz) mushrooms,
    sliced
350 g jar of Madhur Jaffrey's
    Sabzi vegetable curry sauce
100 g (3½ oz) baby spinach

1. Spray a non-stick frying-pan with cooking spray and stir-fry the
beans and mushrooms for 2 – 3 minutes.
2. Add the curry sauce, cover and cook for 10 minutes.
3. Stir in the spinach which will take only a minute or two to wilt
into the curry. Serve.

Points per serving: 4
Total Points per recipe: 8

Cook's note:
Madhur Jaffrey created the sauce for this curry and it's fantastic
with a wide variety of different vegetables.

Variation:
Okra is a good substitute for French beans in this recipe.

Chicken with Courgettes and Pasta

Serves: 2

Preparation and cooking time:
15 minutes
Calories per serving: 305

Freezing: not recommended

This is ideal for using up any leftover meat from a roast chicken. You could also buy some cold pre-cooked chicken breast. Remember to remove the skin since it's full of Calories!

125 g (4½ oz) wholewheat pasta spirals
1 courgette, sliced thinly
100 g (3½ oz) cooked roast chicken, skinned and boned, sliced thinly
2 teaspoons lemon juice
1 tablespoon half-fat crème fraîche
freshly ground black pepper

1. Cook the pasta according to the packet instructions.
2. Meanwhile, steam or microwave the sliced courgette for 4–5 minutes or 3–4 minutes respectively to soften them. Add the sliced chicken and lemon juice and just heat through.
3. Stir the half-fat crème fraîche into the cooked pasta and top with the courgettes and chicken. Season and serve.

Points per serving: 7
Total Points per recipe: 14

Tuna Steak in Soy Sauce

Serves: 2

Preparation and cooking time:
10 minutes + 30 minutes marinating
Calories per serving: 150

Freezing: not recommended

This is wonderful with noodles or a salad in a spicy dressing.

200 g (7 oz) tuna steak, fresh or frozen and defrosted
2 tablespoons soy sauce
2 tablespoons teriyaki marinade
1 teaspoon minced ginger
1 garlic clove, crushed

1. Place the tuna in a shallow bowl and spoon over the soy and teriyaki sauces.
2. Add the ginger and garlic and leave to marinate for 20–30 minutes.
3. Preheat the grill to high.
4. Divide the tuna steak in two and cook under the grill for 7–8 minutes, turning after 4 minutes and basting generously with the marinade.

Points per serving: 2
Total Points per recipe: 4

Cook's note:
Using minced ginger in a jar will save you time and preserve your fingertips from being grazed by a grater.

Speedy Spaghetti

Serves: 2

Preparation and cooking time:
15 minutes
Calories per serving: 440

Freezing: not recommended

You can rely on this recipe when you are very busy and need to rustle up a tasty meal in minutes.

175 g (6 oz) spaghetti
225 g (8 oz) canned chopped tomatoes
1 teaspoon tomato purée
1 garlic clove, crushed
a pinch of oregano
1 teaspoon chilli flakes or chilli powder
185 g can of tuna in spring water or brine, drained and rinsed

1. Cook the spaghetti according to the packet instructions.
2. Meanwhile make the sauce by gently heating together the canned tomatoes, tomato purée, garlic, oregano and chilli flakes.
3. Flake the tuna meat.
4. When the spaghetti is cooked, drain and mix together with the tuna and the tomato sauce.

Points per serving: 4
Total Points per recipe: 8¹/₂

Thai Fry

Serves: 2

Preparation and cooking time:
20 minutes
Calories per serving: 135

Freezing: not recommended

Extremely delicious but very low in Points! Serve with noodles or rice.

2 tablespoons unsweetened desiccated coconut
100 ml (3¹/₂ fl oz) skimmed milk
low-fat cooking spray
¹/₂ green pepper, de-seeded and cubed
¹/₂ red pepper, de-seeded and cubed
100 g (3¹/₂ oz) green beans, topped and tailed
1 large carrot, cut into matchsticks
1 courgette, cut into matchsticks
2 tablespoons light soy sauce
2 teaspoons Thai red curry paste

1. Measure the coconut into a milk pan and add the milk.
2. Bring to the boil, remove from the heat, cover and leave to marinate for a few minutes, while you prepare the vegetables in steps 3 and 4.
3. Spray a non-stick frying-pan with the cooking spray and stir-fry the vegetables.
4. Stir in the soy sauce and curry paste.
5. Strain the milk into the frying-pan and stir-fry for a couple of minutes to give the vegetables a coconut flavour.

Points per serving: 2¹/₂
Total Points per recipe: 5¹/₂

Sweet 'n' Sour Prawns

Serves: 2

Preparation and cooking time: 10 minutes
Calories per serving: 470

Freezing: not recommended

Both small cocktail prawns and large prawns work well in this recipe.

125 g (4½ oz) medium egg noodles
low-fat cooking spray
1 large carrot, cut into matchsticks
4 spring onions, sliced
75 g (2¾ oz) petits pois
160 g jar of sweet and sour stir-fry sauce
200 g (7 oz) small cocktail or large prawns, defrosted

1. Cook the noodles for 4 minutes or according to the packet instructions.
2. Meanwhile, using the cooking spray, stir-fry the carrot matchsticks and spring onions in a non-stick frying-pan.
3. Add the petits pois and sweet and sour sauce. Continue to stir-fry for a further minute.
4. Add the prawns. It is important that the prawns are not overcooked so just heat through.
5. Serve the noodles topped with the prawn and vegetable mixture.

Points per serving: 6½
Total Points per recipe: 13

Cook's note:
Sharwoods make an exceptionally good sweet and sour sauce.

Ham Omelette

Serves: 2

Preparation and cooking time: 10 – 15 minutes
Calories per serving: 290

Freezing: not recommended

Making one omelette instead of two separate ones and then cutting it in half saves Calories because you need less oil.

4 eggs, beaten
1 teaspoon oil
2 slices (70 g/2½ oz) honey roast ham, diced
8 teaspoons fat-free Weight Watchers from Heinz mayonnaise-style dressing
4 teaspoons skimmed milk
1 teaspoon white wine vinegar
200 g (7 oz) crispy salad (with white cabbage)
salt and freshly ground black pepper

1. Season the eggs and heat the oil in a non-stick frying-pan.
2. Pour in the eggs and let them cook, drawing the mixture from the sides of the pan so that the uncooked mixture can run underneath and cook. It should only take 2 – 3 minutes for the omelette to set.
3. Sprinkle with the diced ham, fold one side over the other and divide between two plates.
4. Beat together the mayonnaise, skimmed milk and white wine vinegar. Dress the salad, season and serve with the omelette.

Points per serving: 5½
Total Points per recipe: 11½

Cook's note:
You can buy a ready-prepared crispy salad with cabbage in the supermarket. The crunchiness of the cabbage adds a nice texture to the omelette.

Cod with Parsley Sauce

Serves: 2

Preparation and cooking time:
if using the microwave
15 minutes; if using the
oven 50 minutes
Calories per serving: 135

Freezing: not recommended

2 × 100 g (3½ oz) frozen
chunky cod fillets
1 tablespoon cornflour
150 ml (5 fl oz) skimmed milk
1 tablespoon finely chopped
fresh parsley
salt and freshly ground black
pepper

**A new way to cook an old
favourite.**

1. You can either microwave or poach the cod fillets. To microwave, place the cod fillets in a microwave dish and cover loosely. Cook for 5–6 minutes until the fish is cooked through. To poach them, place in a small ovenproof dish. Cover with water and cook at Gas Mark 5/190°C/375°F for 35–40 minutes.
2. Meanwhile make the parsley sauce. Blend the cornflour with 1 tablespoon of the milk, heat the rest of the milk and then stir in your cornflour paste. Stir while the sauce thickens and cooks. Remove from the heat, add the parsley and season.
3. Serve the cod fillets coated with the sauce.

Points per serving: 2½
Total Points per recipe: 4½

Cook's note:
Adding 1 teaspoon of lemon juice to the sauce really enhances the flavour.

Fish with Lemon and Cucumber Salsa

Serves: 2

Preparation and cooking time:
if using the microwave
10 minutes; if using the
oven 35–40 minutes
Calories per serving: 85

Freezing: not recommended

2 × 100 g (3½ oz) frozen
chunky cod fillets
5 cm (2-inch) piece of
cucumber, diced finely
4 spring onions, sliced finely
2 tablespoons lemon juice
freshly ground black pepper

**Prepare the salsa while you
are cooking the fish so that it
will retain its crisp texture
and fresh, tangy taste until
you are ready to dish up.**

1. Place the cod fillets in a microwave dish and cover loosely. Cook for 5 or 6 minutes until the fish is cooked through or poach the fillets by putting them in a small, ovenproof dish, covering them with water and cooking at Gas Mark 5/190°C/375°F for 35–40 minutes.
2. Meanwhile prepare the salsa by mixing all the remaining ingredients together and seasoning well.
3. When the fish is cooked, serve with the salsa on the side.

Points per serving: 1½
Total Points per recipe: 3

Turkey Kebabs

Serves: 2

Preparation and cooking time:
15 minutes + 30 minutes – 1
hour marinating time
Calories per serving: 105

Freezing: recommended

**Try cooking these on the
barbecue – the flavour is
just wonderful.**

2 tablespoons soy sauce
juice of half a lime
1 garlic clove, crushed
1 teaspoon runny honey
200 g (7 oz) medium boneless,
   skinless turkey breast, cut
   into 12 equal-sized pieces
1/2 red pepper, cut into
   10 equal-sized pieces

1. In a small bowl, mix together the soy sauce, lime juice, garlic
and honey.
2. Mix in the turkey and red pepper. Leave to marinate for at
least 30 minutes and up to an hour.
3. Preheat the grill. Thread the turkey and red pepper on to
2 skewers starting with the turkey and alternating the two all
the way to the end.
4. Grill for 8–10 minutes, turning after 5 minutes. The turkey
should be cooked through and starting to blacken at the edges.

Points per serving: 21/2
Total Points per recipe: 5

Eggs with Curried Dressing

Serves: 2

Preparation and cooking time:
15 minutes
Calories per serving: 120

Freezing: not recommended

V if using free-range eggs

2 eggs
1 teaspoon medium balti curry paste
2 teaspoons lemon juice
100 ml (3½ fl oz) very low-fat plain fromage frais

Eggs and curry are a dynamite duo.

1. Put the eggs into a saucepan of water, bring to the boil and cook for 10 minutes. Then plunge the eggs into cold water to cool.
2. Meanwhile, make the dressing by mixing together the remaining ingredients.
3. Peel the cooled eggs, slice lengthways and place on serving plates. Serve with the sauce spooned over them.

Points per serving: 2
Total Points per recipe: 4

Coronation Chicken Potatoes

Serves: 2

Preparation and cooking time:
15 minutes + 10 minutes cooking (if using a microwave) or 1–1½ hours cooking (if using an oven)
Calories per serving: 240

Freezing: not recommended

Served with a side salad, these potatoes are an excellent midweek treat.

2 baking potatoes (about 175 g/ 6 oz each)
2 tablespoons 90% fat-free Weight Watchers from Heinz mayonnaise-style dressing
½–1 teaspoon medium balti curry paste
a dash of Worcestershire sauce
½ teaspoon lemon juice
2 teaspoons half-fat crème fraîche
100 g (3½ oz) cold cooked chicken, skinned, boned and diced
freshly ground black pepper

1. Prick the potatoes and cook in the microwave for 10–12 minutes until cooked through or cook in a conventional oven at Gas Mark 6/ 200°C/400°F for 1–1½ hours.
2. While the potatoes are cooking, whisk together all of the sauce ingredients, season and then mix in the chicken.
3. When the potatoes are cooked, cut a cross in the top of each and spoon the chicken and sauce into each potato.

Points per serving: 4
Total Points per recipe: 7½

Cook's note:
The topping can be used to stuff mini pitta breads or fill sandwiches. The Points per serving of the filling are 1½.

Variation:
Add 1 tablespoon of mango chutney to your portion. This will add 1 Point.

Fancy Fried Fish

Serves: 2

Preparation and cooking time: 15 minutes
Calories per serving: 205

Freezing: not recommended

You can substitute any white fish fillets for the cod in this mouth-watering recipe.

2 teaspoons whole black peppercorns (crushed lightly)
2 teaspoons plain flour mixed with a little salt and a pinch of paprika
2 × 150 g (5½ oz) fresh cod fillets
2 teaspoons extra-virgin olive oil
4 tablespoons Italian fat-free vinaigrette with garlic
2 teaspoons whole-grain mustard
juice of half a lemon

1. Place the peppercorns, seasoned flour and fish fillets in a plastic bag. Shake gently to coat the fish.
2. Heat the oil and fry the fish for 3–4 minutes on each side.
3. Add the other ingredients to the pan. Stir well while it sizzles and then serve.

Points per serving: 3½
Total Points per recipe: 7

Cook's note:
The Kraft Italian Vinaigrette is especially good.

Tuna Salad

Serves: 2

Preparation time: 10 minutes
Calories per serving: 205

Freezing: not recommended

This is a great way to use up any cooked vegetables in your refrigerator.

1 packet of salad leaves (2–3 servings)
150 g (5½ oz) cooked green vegetables such as broccoli or green beans
4 tomatoes, cut into wedges
100 g (3½ oz) canned sweetcorn
185 g can of tuna in brine, rinsed and drained
For the dressing:
2 teaspoons extra-virgin olive oil
2 tablespoons lemon juice
1 teaspoon Dijon mustard
salt and freshly ground black pepper

1. Arrange the salad leaves in serving bowls and divide the green vegetables, tomatoes, sweetcorn and tuna between them.
2. Put all the dressing ingredients into a screw-top jar with 2 tablespoons of water and shake well. Dress the salad and serve.

Points per serving: 2½
Total Points per recipe: 5½

Cook's note:
You could substitute 200 g (7 oz) fresh tuna steak for the canned tuna and then grill for 3–4 minutes on each side. The Points will be 3 per serving.

Dressings and Side Dishes

These delicious, low-fat dressings are sure to liven up any salad or vegetable dish and the side dishes are guaranteed to add pizzaz to main meals. What could be nicer than a simple green salad with some French dressing drizzled on top or some potatoes in Creamy Chive Dressing? Cool down a hot Indian curry with a refreshing Indian side salad and enjoy the Vegetable Bake with anything you please. Just remember to count the Points!

Spicy Chilli Dressing

Serves: 2

Preparation time: 5 minutes
Calories per serving: 30

Freezing: not recommended

For those who like something spicy to jazz up a salad!

1 teaspoon extra-virgin olive oil
2 teaspoons red wine vinegar
1 tablespoon tomato sauce
1 teaspoon chilli sauce

1. Put all the ingredients in a screw-top jar with 1 tablespoon of water and shake.

Points per serving: 1/2
Total Points per recipe: 1

French Dressing

Serves: 1

Preparation time: 5 minutes
Calories per serving: 50

Freezing: not recommended

A low-calorie version of a classic dressing.

1 teaspoon extra-virgin olive oil
1 tablespoon lemon juice
1/2 teaspoon of Dijon mustard
salt and freshly ground black
    pepper

1. Put all the ingredients in a screw-top jar or small bowl with 1 tablespoon of water and shake or whisk together.

Points per serving: 1
Total Points per recipe: 1

Mustard Vinaigrette

Serves: 2

Preparation time: 5 minutes
Calories per serving: 30

Freezing: not recommended

This is especially good with green salads.

1 teaspoon extra-virgin olive oil
2 teaspoons red wine vinegar
1 teaspoon whole-grain
  mustard

1. Put all of the ingredients in a screw-top jar with 2 tablespoons of water and shake well.

Points per serving: 1/2
Total Points per recipe: 1

Creamy Chive Dressing

Serves: 2

Preparation time: 5 minutes
Calories per serving: 25

Freezing: not recommended

Add some grated carrot and white cabbage and you've just made a delicious coleslaw.

2 tablespoons 90% fat-free
  Weight Watchers from Heinz
  mayonnaise-style dressing
2 tablespoons skimmed milk
1 teaspoon white wine vinegar
1 tablespoon fresh chives,
  chopped finely
freshly ground black pepper

1. Mix together the first four ingredients and season.

Points per serving: 1/2
Total Points per recipe: 1/2

Indian Side Salad

Serves: 2

Preparation time: 5 minutes
+ 15 minutes marinating
Calories per serving: 65

Freezing: not recommended

2 extra-large tomatoes
  (beefsteak tomatoes), diced
a few slices of red onion, diced
2 tablespoons unsweetened
  desiccated coconut
juice of ¹/₂ lemon

**A refreshing side salad for
curry dishes.**

1. Mix together all of the ingredients and leave to marinate for
15 minutes.

Points per serving: 2
Total Points per recipe: 4

Indian Rice

Serves: 2

Preparation and cooking time:
30 minutes
Calories per serving: 265

Freezing: not recommended

125 g (4¹/₂ oz) basmati rice
1 teaspoon oil or butter
¹/₂ teaspoon whole coriander
  seeds
¹/₂ teaspoon whole cumin seeds
¹/₂ teaspoon whole cardamom
  seeds
300 ml (10 fl oz) vegetable
  stock made with 1 stock
  cube and boiling water

**An excellent side dish for all
sorts of curries.**

1. Put the rice in a sieve and run lots of cold water though it or
leave to soak (see Cook's note).
2. Heat the oil or butter in a frying-pan and quickly stir-fry the
spices in it. Only a brief frying is needed to release the flavours
so don't overdo it or you will get a burnt flavour.
3. Add the rice and stock and bring to the boil.
4. Stir, cover with a tight-fitting lid and simmer gently for 10 minutes
to let the rice cook and absorb the stock.
5. Take the pan off the heat and let stand for 10 minutes. Stir
through before serving.

Points per serving: 3¹/₂
Total Points per recipe: 7

Cook's note:
If you have time and would like to make the rice especially light
and fluffy, soak it for 30 minutes in cold water, rinse and proceed
to step 2.

Vegetable Bake

Serves: 4

Preparation time: 10 minutes
+ 20 minutes cooking
Calories per serving: 75

Freezing: not recommended

This is delicious with plain grilled meats or fish.

2 × 400 g (14 oz) canned
   chopped tomatoes
2 tablespoons tomato purée
1 teaspoon dried thyme
low-fat cooking spray
200 g (7 oz) mushrooms, sliced
4 tomatoes, sliced
1 or 2 courgettes, sliced
2 teaspoons extra-virgin olive
   oil
salt and freshly ground black
   pepper

1. Preheat the oven to Gas Mark 7/220°C/425°F.
2. Place the canned tomatoes, tomato purée and thyme in a saucepan and simmer for 5 minutes.
3. Spray a non-stick frying-pan with cooking spray and stir-fry the mushrooms for 2–3 minutes.
4. Mix the tomato sauce and mushrooms together, season and place in a shallow casserole or lasagne dish.
5. Arrange the fresh tomatoes and courgettes in alternating layers on top of the tomatoes and mushrooms and then drizzle with the oil.
6. Bake in the oven for 20–25 minutes, until starting to blacken at the edges.

Points per serving: 1/2
Total Points per recipe: 2

Variation:
For a vegetarian main dish, add a 440 g can of chick peas. Stir in with the tomato sauce in step 4. The Points per serving will be 2. If you top it with 150 g (5½ oz) half-fat grated cheese, the Points per serving will be 6½.

Microwave Potatoes

Serves: 4

Preparation and cooking time:
30 minutes
Calories per serving: 115

Freezing: not recommended

600 g (1 lb 5 oz) potatoes,
   peeled and sliced finely
200 ml (7 fl oz) vegetable stock
   made with 1 stock cube and
   boiling water
freshly ground black pepper

**Serve sprinkled with some
ground cayenne pepper or
some chopped fresh parsley.**

1. Place the potatoes in a shallow microwave-safe dish and pour over the stock. Season.
2. Cover and cook for 15–20 minutes until the potatoes are cooked and have absorbed most of the stock.
3. Leave to stand for 10 minutes before serving.

Points per serving: 1¹/₂
Total Points per recipe: 6¹/₂

Cook's note:
Slicing potatoes can be done quickly if you have a food processor with a slicing attachment.

Variation:
This can be turned into a vegetarian main course by sprinkling the cooked dish with 150 g (5¹/₂ oz) grated cheese and grilling it until the cheese is bubbling and brown. Points per serving will be 6.

Chinese Noodles

Serves: 2

Preparation and cooking time:
5 minutes
Calories per serving: 265

Freezing: not recommended

125 g (4¹/₂ oz) medium egg
   noodles
100 g (3¹/₂ oz) canned
   sweetcorn
2 tablespoons rich soy sauce
1 teaspoon sweet chilli sauce

**A spicy accompaniment – ideal
with any Chinese dish.**

1. Cook the noodles for 4 minutes or according to the packet instructions.
2. Drain the noodles and mix in the sweetcorn, soy sauce and chilli sauce. (There is no need to pre-heat the sweetcorn, unless it has been in the fridge).

Points per serving: 3¹/₂
Total Points per recipe: 7

Desserts

You deserve a treat! So here are some delicious desserts to enjoy. You can whip them up in minutes and enjoy them knowing that they are low-fat and healthy. The recipes all have fruit but they have other goodies such as chocolate, hazelnuts and pastry too. Simple, satisfying and superb!

Hazelnut and Honey-Stuffed Apple

Serves: 1

Preparation and cooking time: 10 minutes
Calories per serving: 130

Freezing: not recommended

1 dessert apple, cored and scored around the middle
1 teaspoon roasted chopped hazelnuts
1 teaspoon raisins
1 teaspoon runny honey

Hazelnuts and honey are a divine combination.

1. Put the apple in a small microwave-safe container.
2. Mix the remaining ingredients together and spoon into the cored apple.
3. Microwave for 2 minutes. Leave to stand for 7 minutes before serving.

Points per serving: 2
Total Points per recipe: 2

Cook's note:
If you want to use a conventional oven, put the apple in a lightly greased baking dish. Bake for 45–60 minutes at Gas Mark 4/ 180°C/350°F until the apple is soft and fluffy.

Pear and Chocolate Layers

Serves: 2

Preparation time: 15 minutes + 30 minutes cooling
Calories per serving: 240

Freezing: not recommended

4 ripe dessert pears, cored, skinned and diced
2 × 55 g pots of Weight Watchers from Heinz chocolate mousse
1 tablespoon toasted sliced almonds

Both adults and children alike adore this treat.

1. Place the pears in a small saucepan with a little water. Bring to the boil, cover and simmer for 4 or 5 minutes until soft. Drain well and leave to cool for 30 minutes.
2. Purée the pears once they are cool.
3. Divide half of the purée among two small ramekin dishes and cover with half of the chocolate mousse. Cover with the rest of the purée and then top with the remaining mousse.
4. Sprinkle with the almonds and serve immediately.

Points per serving: 4
Total Points per recipe: 8

Nectarines Baked in Wine

Serves: 4

Preparation time: 5 minutes + 25 minutes cooking + cooling

Calories per serving: 130

Freezing: not recommended

4 nectarines, ripe and ready to eat
200 ml (7 fl oz) red wine (any sort)
2 tablespoons sugar

A delicious summer dessert which is impressive on special occasions and at dinner parties.

1. Preheat the oven to Gas Mark 6/200°C/400°F.
2. Cut the nectarines in half and remove the stones.
3. Place in a shallow ovenproof dish and pour over the wine.
4. Sprinkle with the sugar and bake in the oven for 25 minutes.
5. Cool slightly so you don't burn your mouth and when ready to serve, divide between the serving dishes and spoon over the remaining wine in the dishes.

Points per serving: 1½
Total Points per recipe: 7

Cook's note:
To remove the skins from the nectarines, place them in a bowl, cover with boiling water and leave for 30 seconds. Drain. The skins will peel off very easily.

Variation:
Replace the red wine with white wine and a tablespoon of elderflower cordial.

Raspberries and Redcurrants in Blackberry Sauce

Serves: 4

Preparation time: 10 minutes + 30 minutes cooling

Calories per serving: 25

Freezing: not recommended

115 g (4 oz) blackberries
artificial sweetener, to taste
115 g (4 oz) raspberries
115 g (4 oz) redcurrants, stripped from the stalks

Make this when summer fruits are abundant. You can liquidise the sauce if you want but it's especially nice with chunks of fruit in it.

1. Place the blackberries in a small saucepan with 2 tablespoons of water. Bring to the boil and simmer for 3 minutes. As it simmers, squash down the fruit to make a chunky sauce. Sweeten to taste and leave to cool.
2. To serve, divide the raspberries and redcurrants equally between the serving bowls and top with the cooled blackberry sauce.

Points per serving: ½
Total Points per recipe: 1½

Cook's note:
Serve with a scoop of low-fat ice-cream per person for a real treat. Remember to add the extra Points.

Filo-Wrapped Treats

Makes: 12

Preparation and cooking time:
20 minutes
Calories per serving: 50

Freezing: not recommended

4 filo pastry sheets (25 cm/
10 inches square)
2 medium bananas, each sliced
into 12
40 g (1¹/₂ oz) raisins
low-fat cooking spray

**These are incredibly delicious
and very easy to make.**

1. Preheat the oven to Gas Mark 6/200°C/400°F.
2. Cut each sheet of filo pastry lengthways into three strips.
3. Place 2 slices of banana and a few raisins at the bottom of each filo strip, leaving a slight border between the left and right side and also at the bottom.
4. Fold the right hand bottom corner of each strip over the banana and raisin filling so that it forms a triangle when it touches the other side. Now fold the triangle up over itself and keep on folding until you have a little triangular package. Repeat with each strip of pastry. Place the filo triangles on a baking sheet.
5. Spray the little triangles with some cooking spray.
6. Bake in the oven for 15 minutes until golden brown. Eat while still warm.

Points per serving: ¹/₂
Total Points per recipe: 8¹/₂

Chocolate Mousse with Nut 'n' Cherry Topping

Serves: 4

Preparation time: 5 minutes
Calories per serving: 150

Freezing: not recommended

4 chocolate dessert cups
4 × 55 g (2 oz) diet chocolate
mousse
4 teaspoons roasted chopped
hazelnuts
2 glacé cherries, halved

These are worth every Point!

1. Place a dessert cup on a serving plate and fill each one with the contents of one tub of chocolate mousse.
2. Sprinkle with the roasted chopped hazelnuts and top each with a halved glacé cherry. Serve.

Points per serving: 3¹/₂
Total Points per recipe: 13¹/₂

Yogurty Fruit Trifle

Serves: 6

Preparation time: 10 minutes
Calories per serving: 180

Freezing: not recommended

A great trifle for family and friends.

1 tablespoon low-calorie raspberry jam
4 trifle sponges, halved
150 ml (5 fl oz) medium sherry
125 g (4½ oz) strawberries, sliced
4 ripe passion fruit, halved
400 ml (14 fl oz) vanilla-flavoured very low-fat plain yogurt
6 tablespoons whipping cream

1. Spread the jam over half of the trifle sponges, then sandwich together and place in the bottom of a large trifle bowl.
2. Pour the sherry all over the trifle sponges.
3. Place the strawberries over the sponges and spoon over the passion fruit.
4. Cover with the vanilla yogurt, decorate with the swirls of cream and serve immediately.

Points per serving: 3½
Total Points per recipe: 20½

Cook's note:
You can substitute fresh orange juice for some or all of the sherry. Look for the reduced-fat whipped cream in an aerosol can near the cream in the supermarket.

Mini Summer Puddings

Serves: 4

Preparation and cooking time: 15 minutes + 20 minutes cooling time
Calories per serving: 90

Freezing: not recommended

This is an excellent summer pudding – ideal for when all these fruits are abundant; you can also make it during the winter using frozen summer fruits.

low-fat cooking spray
4 thin slices of white bread
115 g (4 oz) redcurrants
115 g (4 oz) blackcurrants
50 g (1¾ oz) raspberries
artificial sweetener, to taste

1. Preheat the oven to Gas Mark 6/200°C/400°F.
2. Spray 4 ramekins or deep bun tins very lightly with the cooking spray.
3. Cut 4 large circles out of the bread and shape these into your ramekins or bun tins.
4. Place in the oven and bake for 10 minutes.
5. Meanwhile, place the fruit in a small saucepan with 100 ml (3½ fl oz) of water and gently heat. Cook for a few minutes to soften the fruit and release the juices. Sweeten to taste and leave to cool.
6. Carefully remove the cooked bread cases from the ramekins or bun tins. Brush each case with some of the fruit juices so that they turn a lovely red colour. Leave to stand.
7. When everything is cool, place the bread cases on 4 individual serving plates and top with the fruit, spooning the juices around them. Serve immediately.

Points per serving: 1
Total Points per recipe: 4½

Index